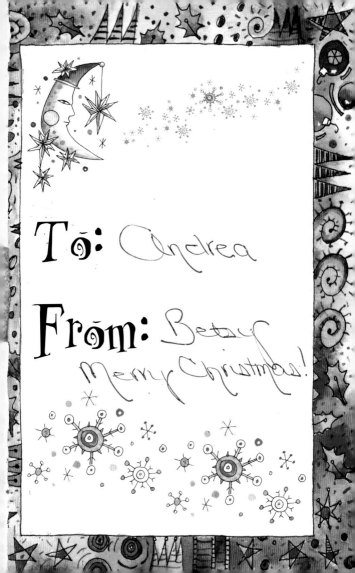

To: Andrea

From: Betsy
Merry Christmas!

A Bit of
Applause

for
Mrs. Claus

A Bit of Applause for Mrs. Claus

Jeannie Schick-Jacobowitz ★ Susie Schick-Pierce
Muffin Drake ★ Illustrated by Wendy Wallin Malinow

SOURCEBOOKS, INC.®
NAPERVILLE, ILLINOIS

This book is dedicated to:

Genevieve Bowman Schick, the
"tired Mrs. Claus" behind our
own sweetheart of a Santa,
E.H. Schick, Sr.

And to all the other Mrs. Claus'
for the holiday festivities,
traditions, and celebrations
which do not come
about by sheer magic.

We applaud you!

Twas the night after Christmas
and time for a pause;
Collapsed in the corner
sat tired Mrs. Claus.

The stockings were crooked,
the house was a mess;
The tree had tipped over—
she couldn't care less!

Her muscles were aching, her feet were so sore; This overworked spouse couldn't take any more!

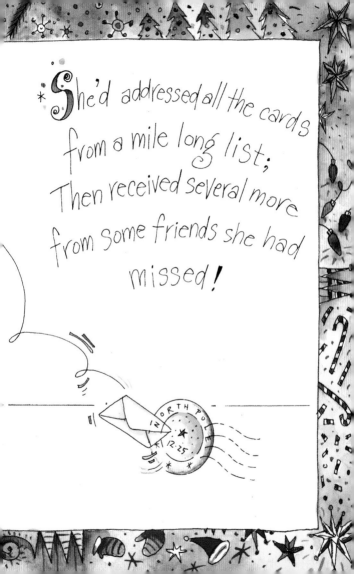

She'd addressed all the cards
from a mile long list;
Then received several more
from some friends she had
missed!

With the elves she'd wrapped
presents for many nights through,
With tape on their fingers,
bows, paper, and glue.

When she'd lifted her nose,
turned her head to the side,
She had smelled something burning...
"My cookies!" she'd cried!

She was chubby and plump,
quite a jolly ol' soul,
From testing each goody
and licking the bowl.

At last all was done
by the skin of her teeth,
The mistletoe hung
with the holly and wreath!

Then Santa had cried
as he left on his flight,
"You're the greatest, my dear!
Merry Christmas!
Good night!"

The elves were all sleeping,
each tucked into bed;

But visions and fantasies
danced in her head!

Come next year, no more baking
or trimming the tree;
On the beach with the elves –
that is where she would be!

And then she envisioned
a gorgeous new sable;
With emeralds and rubies
hung down to her navel!

When up on the roof
there arose such a clatter,
It ended her dreaming...
"Now, what is the matter?"

Away to the window she flew like a flash;
As she tripped on the clutter, hopped over the trash.

When what to her weary red
eyes did appear,
But the emptied out sleigh
and eight hungry reindeer!

And the little old driver
so lively and quick,
Was worn out by his travels—
Could this be St. Nick?

"Will you see to the reindeer, my darling?" he said.

Kissed his wife, said "I love you," and took to his bed.

"Now Dasher, now Dancer,

now Prancer and Vixen;

"Here Comet, here Cupid, here Donner and Blitzen."

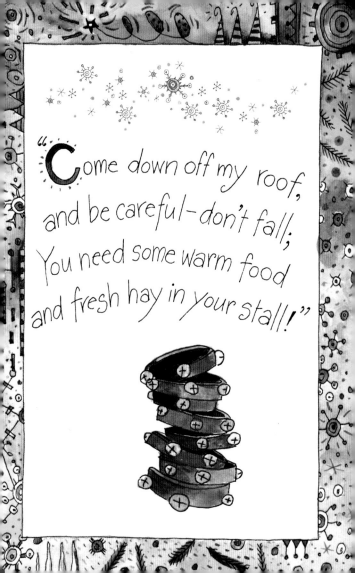

"Come down off my roof,
and be careful—don't fall;
You need some warm food
and fresh hay in your stall!"

"Well done, deer,"
she said fondly,
though standing there freezin'
Her thoughts then returned
to her efforts this season.

She had toiled all day long and was covered with soot, And her clothing was stained from her head to her foot.

She spoke not a word,
for she felt quite berserk,
As she heaved a big sigh...
she had done so much work!

Then she flopped in a chair
with no breath left to whistle;
A smile on her face
made her finally look blissful!

Mrs. Claus could still smile
as she relived these scenes;
For she knew of her part
in fulfilling our dreams!

Santa Claus gets the credit
though everyone knows,
Mrs. Claus is the one
who deserves hallowed prose!

So let's give a cheer for
our own Mrs. Claus;
Her love and her work
rate a special applause!